TRINITY
COLLEGE LONDON PRESS

C000148568

GRADE

04

PIANO

Pieces & Exercises for
Trinity College London
Exams 2018–2020

Published by
Trinity College London Press Ltd
trinitycollege.com

Registered in England
Company no. 09726123

Printed in England by Caligraving Ltd

Minuet in E major

Johann Philipp Kirnberger
(1721-1783)

Play the repeats in the exam.

Allegretto

from *The London Sketchbook*, K. 15hh

Wolfgang Amadeus Mozart
(1756-1791)

5

Barcarolle
op. 100 no. 22

Friedrich Burgmüller
(1806-1874)

poco rall.

In tempo

lusingando

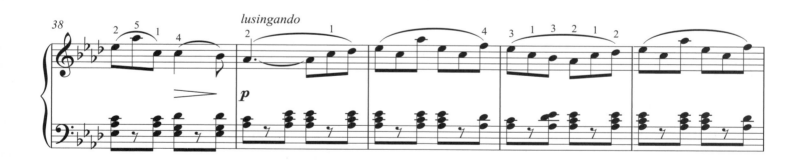

perdendosi

Andantino

First movement from *Sonatina*

Edward Elgar
(1857-1934)

Little Piece no. 17

from *20 Little Pieces for Beginners*, op. 6

Aleksandr Gedike
(1877–1957)

Por una cabeza

Arr. Farrington

Carlos Gardel
(1890-1935)

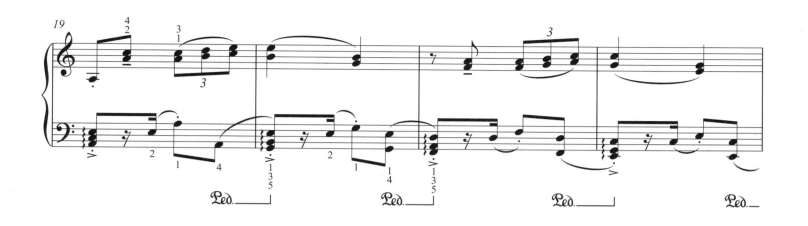

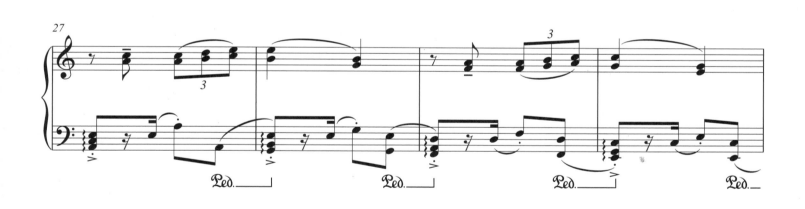

[Blank page to facilitate page turns]

Ballo gaio

Henk Badings
(1907-1987)

Waltz mystique

Ray Moore
(b. 1939)

The repeat must be played in the exam.

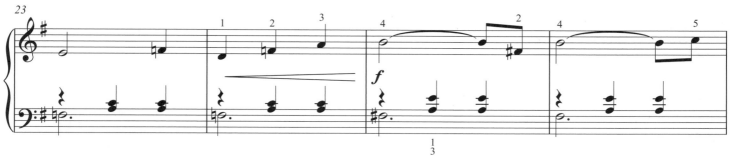

Tango passionis

Barbara Arens
(b. 1960)

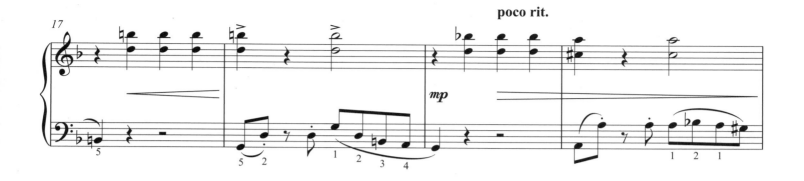

Exercises

1a. Little Waltz – tone, balance and voicing

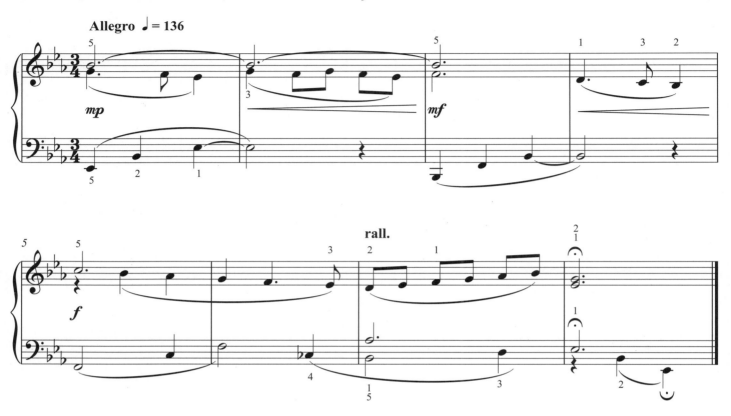

1b. Evening Sun – tone, balance and voicing

20

2a. Waltz Echoes – co-ordination

2b. A Walk in the Woods – co-ordination

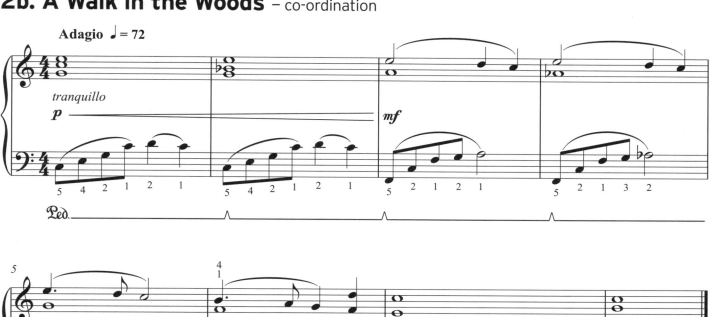

3a. Timelines *– finger & wrist strength and flexibility*

3b. Roll up, roll up! *– finger & wrist strength and flexibility*